# Green Shoots Rising

# Andy Tooze

ILLUSTRATED BY MARTIN OLSSON

Matador
9 Priory Business Park,
Wistow Road, Kibworth Beauchamp,
Leicestershire. LE8 0RX
Tel: 0116 279 2299
Email: books@troubador.co.uk
Web: www.troubador.co.uk/matador
Twitter: @matadorbooks

ISBN 978 1800461 536

British Library Cataloguing in Publication Data.
A catalogue record for this book is available from the British Library.

Printed and bound by CPI Group (UK) Ltd, Croydon, CR0 4YY
Typeset in 14pt Aldine401 BT by Troubador Publishing Ltd, Leicester, UK

Matador is an imprint of Troubador Publishing Ltd

Many thanks to Connie Tooze,
Beth Tooze and Daniel Kearley for their
help in editing this book.

# Andy Tooze

www.thepoetfromthepeaks.co.uk

# contents

## Green For Go

## Schools

## Animals

# Kennings, Riddles And Tongue Twisters

# Dreams

# Friends And Family

# Bodies

# Wordplay And Wildness

# Twenty Words

# The World Of Books

# Sports And Hobbies

# Green For Ever

# Green For Go

## Green Shoots Rising

On this wonderful planet of ours
Nearly everyone agrees
That we can't go on like this
With melting ice caps and rising seas.

The wave of change is rolling,
So it's not at all surprising
That this is the time to see and to be
The green shoots rising.

# Salmony, Sharky, Tuna And Me

We are all different fish
Swimming in the same sea.
Salmony, Sharky,
Tuna and me.

If there's one thing we know
About life in the sea
It's that we're all different.
Fishy diversity.

We've been here a long while,
Many millions of years.
You'd think we were undefeatable
But we do have our fears.

All this poisonous plastic!
It keeps getting worse.
You not only eat us,
You send a plastic curse.

So sort yourselves out,
Stop sending us pollution.
Please, please, please,
Find a solution.

We may be different fish,
But we all swim in the same sea.
Salmony,
Sharky,
Tuna
And me.

# Winter's coming

Piggy Wig wore a wig,
Which he combed with a twig
That he found on the ground,
In a hole with some coal,
Which he burned when he learned
That winter was coming soon.

So Piggy Wig snuggled up
With a hot chocolate cup,
As he combed his wig with a twig
That he found on the ground,
In a hole with some coal,
Which he burned when he learned
That winter was coming soon.

And Piggy Wig was wise,
For it started to snow
That very afternoon.

4

# The Most Magical Music

There's percussion in our gardens
And woodwind in the wood.
There's always music to be heard
In our tree filled neighbourhood.

Crows jabber raucously.
Robins' high notes trill.
The music played by nature
Always gives a thrill.

Even after dark
Winds whistle while owls hoot.
There's more to glean from gardens
Than flowers, veg and fruit.

Oh yes we love our instruments
Which we pluck and beat and blow,
But the most magical music is outside,
Please listen, then you'll know.

# Night Lights

Starlight
>Moonlight
>>Just right!

Bright lights
>Night lights
>>Light nights.

Starlight
>Moonlight
>>Just right!

6

# Giants

Soaring upwards,
Cascading outwards,
Spreading under the ground.

Rooted in the soil,
Forever branching out,
Our trees are all around.

These living
Breathing giants
Who dominate our land.

We exchange gases,
Share lives,
Together, branch in hand.

# First Frost

First frost falls,
Jack Frost calls.

Blue up high,
Cloudless sky.

Tingly toes,
Chilly nose.

Bobble hat,
Indoor cat.

Birds puff up,
Hot chocolate cup.

Clouds of steam,
Icy dream.

Heat long past,
Autumn can't last.

First frost falls,
Jack Frost calls.

# Our Island

We live on an island
Surrounded by the sea.
Our seas are rather chilly
And although some chillies are ever so hot,
The seas around Great Britain
Are definitely not!

# Schools

## Maths

If two and two is always four,
And four and four is eight,
Why can I never remember these facts
Until it's far too late?

Is my brain too small?
Or
Are numbers just too long?
I'd rather paint a picture
Or

     sing

         a

       silly

         song!

# General Dog

General Dog,
Our strange head teacher.
General Dog,
A large, hairy creature.
General Dog,
Leaps about.
General Dog,
If you can, get out!
General Dog,
He's so bad.
General Dog,
Barking mad!

# Our School's Like The Army

Commando crawling in the library,
Press ups in the playground.
Our school's like the army.

Monday morning parachute drops,
Lunchtime marching never stops.
Our school's like the army.

Left right, left right,
We hear it in our dreams at night.
Our school's like the army.

Our uniform is camouflage khaki,
The headteacher's known as Sergeant Sparky.
Our school's like the army.

Food rations are really grim,
Cold baked beans from a giant tin.
Our school's like the army.

The teachers all arrive in tanks,
Would I drive one? No thanks!
Our school's like the army.

I don't know what we're training for,
Sparky tells us: "School is war."
Our school's like the army.

# Playground Strut

She's the boss of the playground.
The teacher with style.
She glides as she slides
With her permagrin smile.

Any fight she can stop
With one loud finger click,
Or her lion deep growl,
She owns every trick.

To the good and the worthy
She is their protector.
To the wicked and naughty
She's a damage detector.

Nothing gets past her
She's inside your brain.
She knows every scheme
Of those who cause pain.

No excuses accepted,
Not an if or a but.
She's the queen of the school
With her playground strut!

# Morning At The School Gate

A cuddle goodbye, a wave, a kiss.
A new day starts where we know we will miss
All those we love who make our hearts swell,
Who know us deeply and love us so well,
Who always make us feel so at home
That we never ever feel truly alone.
For to feel that we truly, deeply belong,
Is to feel that our world can never go wrong.

So we stash away the treasure
Of the goodbye kiss
And stride through the school gates,
"Good morning Miss."

16

# On A chair

It's your own secret lair:
On a chair.
Put aside every care:
On a chair.
Display so much flair:
On a chair.
Just comb your hair:
On a chair.
Munch on a pear:
On a chair.
Admirers will stare:
On a chair.
But always watch out:
On a chair.
For if it's going spare:
On a chair.
Just beware:
On a chair.
Or you'll find someone there:
On your chair!

# The School Week

Manic Monday,
Traumatic Tuesday,
Woeful Wednesday,
Thumping Thursday,
Frightful Friday,
Sit around Saturday,
Stay in bed Sunday
And repeat…
Until the next school holiday!

# School Disco

School disco: Time to flow.
School disco: Go, go, go.
School disco: Bounce and bop.
School disco: Just don't stop.
School disco: Jumping boys.
School disco: Making noise.
School disco: Grooving girls.
School disco: Spins and twirls.
School disco: Take your chance.
School disco: Dance, dance, dance.

# Day Off

Your brain
Is usually helpful,
But not today.
Today is the one
That got away.

Today is the day
When nothing helps.
Today is the day
When your brain yelps,
"Don't bother me,
It's my day off!"

# The Fab Four

Ahead of three,
Just before five,
We find four.

Four quarters and four seasons
Are two of the innumerable reasons
Why four is fab forever.
Will we ever forget four?
Never!

# Animals

## Losing Temo

Temo is my rattlesnake,
He ran away last week.
He slithered out of the house
After playing hide and seek.

His favourite place to hide
Was on our bottom stair.
He would keep quite quiet,
Just flick his tongue and stare.

The pattern on the carpet
Looks like Temo's skin,
So when he lay still
He really blended in.

Sometimes he'd move a little,
I'd hear the faintest rattle.
Then victory was mine,
Triumph in the battle.

Then Temo would look for me,
Sometimes I'd hide in the loo.
I know a few nooks and crannies
But Temo knew them too.

He would slither rapidly
All around the house.
Sometimes he'd find other things,
Once he caught a mouse!

When at last Temo found me
He would rattle with delight,
Excited that this time
He'd won our strange play fight.

When we were both worn out
We'd watch the telly together.
Usually children's TV,
Sometimes the news and weather.

23

But this week Temo's on the news,
Now he's slithered away.
Everyone's looking for my rattlesnake
Who loves to watch telly and play.

I really hope they find him,
I'm missing him like mad.
My sister lent me her tiger
To stop me from being sad.

But he can't play games like Temo,
He doesn't know what to do.
He just charges all over the house.
Oh Temo, I do miss you!

# MY FLY

High in the blue sky
Flies a fly.
My Fly!
I set it free one sunny day,
Without a pause it flew away.
It did not wave, it did not stay,
It simply, quickly, flew away.
You would have thought it didn't care,
It left me there to stand and stare.
For I could not follow,
I could not fly
Away with it into the sky.
My heart was broken,
My face was grey,
The day my fly flew away.
With a lump in my throat
Out came a cry,
"So long, farewell,
Goodbye my fly!"

25

# Mr Mouse

Mr Mouse lives in our house.
He rustles, hustles, bustles,
From dusk to dawn,
From night to morn,
He scurries, hurries,
Eats, defecates.
He is not one of my mates.
He's ever so messy.
He doesn't pay rent.
He leaves everything he gets at
Broken and bent.

# Bugs

Sometimes creep,
Sometimes leap,
Sometimes fly
In the sky.

Sometimes run,
Sometimes crawl,
Up and down
Along a wall.

Sometimes jump,
Sometimes hop,
On the move,
Never stop.

Their teeny, tiny voices call,
"It's a bug's life
After all!"

# Big Bird

Big bird on a bin,
Can't get in,
Too big, not thin,
This big, hungry bird on a bin.

Prises lid open,
Squawks with delight,
Thinks it's won
The bird bin fight.

Loses balance,
Falls in.
Not so clever now,
This big bird in a bin.

Lid slams shut,
It's bin day.
Bin tips up,
Lorry moves away.

Big bird now
Not in bin.
Big bird now
Trapped within.

28

Rumbling lorry
On way to tip,
Big bird in mess
After one costly slip.

Big bird gives
A plaintive squawk,
No one around
To hear it talk.

Lorry reaches tip,
Out the rubbish tumbles.
Lorry off on next job,
Driver gently grumbles.

Big bird covered in rubbish,
Mess and goo.
Big bird feels groggy,
You would too!

Big bird stretches its wings,
Flaps woozily away.
Enough big bird bin battles
For one day.

# Meeting A Llama

I met a llama on a lead,
A lead it didn't really need.
It really wanted to be free.
I knew this as it looked at me.

It bent its head.
The lead slipped off.
The llama spat
And then ran off.

# Seagulls

Seagulls are scavengers.
Not hunters,
Not lions patrolling the savannah
Or sharks patrolling the sea.

Seagulls are scavengers.
Just like you and me
When we're feeling peckish
And there's not much in for tea.

Seagulls are scavengers
And robbers as well.
They stole my daughter's sandwich.
They're the birds from hell!

# Our Dragon Bruce

Our dragon Bruce has just flown by,
High as high across the sky.
Just a speck, so hard to see.
Though not quite so difficult for me.

For Bruce lives in a shed in our garden.
When I mention this people say, "Pardon?
I think I misheard,
Did you say you own a giant bird?"

"No!" I say,
" Not a bird, our dragon Bruce."
"Is it safe," they ask,
"To have a dragon on the loose?"

"Safe?" I say, "I wouldn't say that."
He did munch up the neighbour's cat,
And then their rabbit and hamster as well.
He wasn't even sorry as far as we could tell.

Oh, and he ate my sister's horse,
She was mad about that, of course.
So Bruce is rather a ferocious beast,
Crunching up pets for a dragony feast.

But he's friendlier now. He's found a wife.
She's brought love into his life.
Bruce brings her beautiful bunches of
flowers,
Then sings to her for hours and hours.

Now they've got gorgeous newborn triplets.
Bruce is as loving as a dragon dad gets.
But the babies will need feeding as they
grow…
Oh dear,
Uh oh!

# Kennings, Riddles And Tongue Twisters

## Wally The Wannabe Wallaby

Wally the Wannabe Wallaby
Went to Wannabe Wallaby classes.
But Wally the Wannabe Wallaby
Forgot his wannabe-able-to-see glasses.

Wally the Wannabe Wallaby
Had to practice his wallaby hop.
But Wally couldn't see the sign that said:
WANNABE WALLABIES STOP!

So Wally the Wannabe Wallaby
Tripped and walloped his head.
Wally the Wannabe Wallaby
Fell down like he was dead.

Now Wally the Wannabe Wallaby
Wants to feel less pain.
Wally the Wannabe Wallaby
Wants to feel well again.

So when Wally the Wannabe Wallaby
Next goes to Wannabe Wallaby classes,
He probably won't forgot his
Wannabe-able-to-see glasses!

35

# I can't Think

What do you mean,
You can't think?
You're thinking what to say
Before you say you can't think.
So you clearly can think,
For all I know you may not
Be able to wink or blink,
But you're kicking up a stink
When you say you can't think
Because you clearly can.
Wham! Bam!

# Miss March

Miss March marches madly
Most March days.
Marching madly most March days
Is Miss March's mysterious craze.

Most March days Miss March
Marches around the town.
Marching, marching, marching,
Merrily, up and down.

During non-marching months
Miss March often says,
"I'm missing my magical,
March marching days."

Oh, mysterious, marching
Miss March!

# Riddle Me One

Little pinchers,
Beach roamers,
Wave surfers,
Sideways scuttlers.

Our claws
Pause
For your
Applause.

We live
On the edge
Of the sea.

But who
Are we?

 38

Answer on page 116

# Riddle Me Two

Light splitter,
Arch fitter,
Spectrum coverer,
Gloom smotherer,
Weather masher,
Sunny splasher.

Answer on page 116

# RiddLe Me Three

Child catcher,
Lie-in snatcher,
Friend blender,
Hope sender,
Idea inspirer,
Knowledge enquirer,
Time taker,
Citizen maker.

Answer on page 116

# Riddle Me Four

Colosseum fighters,
Pizza biters,
Armour wearers,
Bath sharers,
Slave keepers,
Coin heapers,
Emperor crowners,
Celt frowners,
Hadrian's wall,
Empires fall.

Answer on page 116

# Dreams

## Imagine

What would I change
If I was in charge for a day?
The usual stuff;
Less work, more play.
World peace for ever,
More tasty curry.
School would start at ten
So I wouldn't need to hurry.
More rain in Africa,
More sunshine here.
Lots more laughter,
A lot less fear.

Loving mums and dads
For every single child.
Lots more discos
Where we could go wild.
Maybe one thing different
From all the usual stuff,
I'd give an award to my belly button
For collecting the most fluff.

# The Other Night

I dreamed,
The other night,
That my friend was a giraffe,
Elegant and refined:
Long necked,
Long legged,
Long nosed.
I supposed
At the time,
My dream was reality.
I woke up,
It wasn't,
I'd returned to normality.

 44

# Hold On

Hold on to what you believe.
Hold on to who you are.
Hold on to those things
    That have served you well so far.

But don't forget to stretch out.
Don't forget to reach.
The world is a life long teacher
    So see what it has to teach.

And above all else,
While enlarging your mind,
Treat others as you would like to be treated.
    In other words: Be kind!

45

# Work Hard

Work hard!
Be kind!
If you do
These two things
You may find
Your soul sings.

# Your Dream

Your dream can be powerful,
More valuable than gold.
It should never be discarded,
Lost or sold.

Your dream can lead you on
Or pull you back.
It can make you take flight,
Or fight and attack.

For your dream is vital.
It's part of you.
It's real, it's free,
It's the key, it's true!

47

# One Kind Word

One kind word
Can make your day.
One kind word
Can show the way.
One kind word
Can make you say,
Hurray!

# connected

A flame on a candle,
A bucket with a handle.

A shoe with a lace,
A smile on a face.

A clock with two hands,
A shell on the sands.

A hand in a glove,
A heart full of love.

# Graffiti

Graffiti is
Words or images placed in the
Wrong place.
A private thought in a
Public space.

Maybe a scrawl
On a wall,
Or a sign
Beside a train line.

Or even a prayer
For the world to care.
Graffiti can be
Anything, anytime, anywhere.

# Friends And Family

## Together

So many friends,
So much fun,
Everyone together,
Basking in the sun.
Struggles crop up
Like weeds from the earth,
But we chop them down
And stifle their rebirth.
For we are unbreakable,
Stronger than steel.
    We love,
        We hope,
            We care,
                We feel.

# My Little Bit of Magic

By Beth Tooze age 9

I have a little magic
I've used since I was one.
You could use it too
If you knew how it was done.

>Everyone can use it,
>There's no need to pay.
>You can spread a little magic
>In your own little way.

It's only a little magic
But it spreads from me to you,
So if you see me using it
You can use it too.

>Everyone can use it,
>There's no need to pay.
>You can spread a little magic
>In your own little way.

It's a very special thing,
It spreads from mile to mile.
If you haven't guessed already
I'll tell you: it's my smile!

Everyone can use it,
There's no need to pay.
You can spread a little magic
In your own little way.

# Family

I like my family,
They like me.
It's as simple as that,
Like a head with a hat
Or a hand with a glove.
Fitting together,
We call it love!

54

# Belonging

We all have a longing
For belonging.
To be known
In a place we call home.
Not knowing our future,
Doesn't matter
When we know our identity
Won't scatter,
Can't shatter,
Because we are loved
And so we matter,
Inordinately.
We are
Out of the ordinary,
Just because
We are US!

55

# That First Friend

When you feel all alone
You get a pain in your chest.
It's the kind of feeling
That's far from the best.

It feels like they're friendly
Except for with you.
You might just be paranoid,
But it might just be true.

So you stretch out for friendship,
You do all that you can.
For getting great mates
Is a vital plan.

But you also know
You're only half of the game.
You need the others
To do the same.

And when someone smiles at you,
It feels so great.
All the pain subsides
When you get your first mate.

But if no one reaches out
And you stay outside,
All you want to do
Is run away and hide.

So please be that first friend,
You know this is true.
You'd love someone to reach out
If the lonely one was you!

# Sparks

Watch the sparks fly
When they don't see eye to eye.
One says, "Stop!"
The other says, "Go!"
One says, "Yes!"
The other says, "No!"
One says, "That's it!"
The other says, "You're right!"
But I just want to beg them,
"Please don't fight."

# Connie The New Born

Too beautiful to be,
Curled up into her initial, C.
This wrinkly, sleepy baby
Is lodged in my memory.
She's apart from
But a part of me.
From here on in
Daddy is my new identity.

# Bodies

## Beware

It's huge, it's scary,
It's horrible and hairy.
It's most unpleasant
In every way.
It lures you in
And murmurs, "Stay!"
Don't take a look
I beg,
I pray.
From your mirror
Keep away!

# Fingers

Rather creasy,
Easily greasy,
Top pointers,
Bendy jointers,
Counting digits,
Puppet midgets,
Finger-licking fun never fails,
**But don't bite your nails!**

# Noses

Noses blow,
Noses are always on show.
Noses run,
Noses go red in the hot, summer sun.
Noses point,
Noses can go out of joint.
Noses drip
Nose stuff onto your lip.
Noses sniff,
Noses know if there's a bad whiff.
Noses are clever,
As the old saying goes,
If you don't know where to go,
Just follow your nose.

# A Gripping Tale

Thumbs are squat and thick.
They may not be nimble and quick,
But thumbs give us grip.
Without grip
We couldn't hold a spoon or a pen,
Or a flint for making fire,
And then…
No chance of humans reaching higher.

**Your Feet**

Tap them to the beat,
Your Feet.
Take your socks off in the heat,
Your Feet.
Paint your toe nails for a treat,
Your Feet.
Send messages with them in a tweet,
Your Feet.
Cover them with chocolate to make them sweet,
Your Feet.
Line them up together to make them neat,
Your Feet.
Call one of them Gracie and the other one Pete,
Your Feet!

# Mouths

If you spread your lips wide
And look inside,
There's a hole containing
A flipperty, flopperty tongue
And teeth,
While down your throat,
There are stranger things
Beneath!

# Twitchy Nose

Twitchy nose, itchy nose,
Ready for a sneeze.
Something's moving up there,
Someone help me please.

Could it be a bug,
Or maybe a fly?
Or maybe some left over
Lunchtime pie?

I shouldn't prod or poke,
I know it's not allowed.
It's not polite to pick your nose
When you're in a crowd.

But it's so itchy and twitchy,
What else can I do?
Ahh! It's fallen out,
It's there by my shoe.

 66

Now something is slowly
Creeping away.
My nose is unblocked,
Everything's okay!

# Wordplay And Wildness

## Bill

Bill's the monster in the classroom,
He sleeps in my mate's drawer.
Bill can change size by blinking.
It's a clever trick for sure.

It comes in really handy
When the teacher rushes in,
Bill blinks to make himself tiny,
Then hides himself in the bin.

Bill loves lying in the bin,
Amongst the mess and goo.
He rolls in it to clean himself,
It's a monstrous thing to do.

But it's Bill's way of washing,
"Monster fun", he squeaks.
He's not really bothered
If in actual fact he reeks!

When the teacher's popped out
And it's just my mates and me,
Bill blinks to become human size
And squeaks, "Wahoo, wahee".

Then he cartwheels around the classroom,
And dangles from the lights.
Or pretends that he's a wrestler,
Throwing us around in fights.

Bill's ever so energetic.
He's kind and funny too.
I'm sure that if you knew him
You'd like him like we do.

But the teachers must not find him.
If they do they'll be blinking mad
And we'll lose our monster friend.
The only one we've ever had.

# Heads

Heads up:
A warning.

Heads down:
Sleep until morning.

Heads or tails:
A coin flick.

Head's gone:
Henry V111's wicked trick.

Head teacher:
The boss.

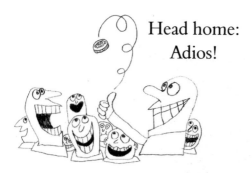

Head home:
Adios!

# Fraggling

Fraggling's fun,
Fraggling's fine,
Fraggling on Fridays is
Fraggtastically divine.

Fraggling's fabulous,
Fraggling's free,
Fraggling's fraggalicious
For fragglers like me.

Fraggling's fantastic,
Fraggling's fast.
Fraggling's finished,
Fraggling's past!

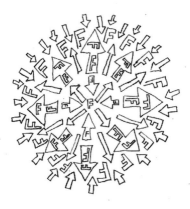

# The Tooth Fairy

The tooth fairy went
On holiday.
Where she went,
She didn't say.

Trailing fairy dust
As her scent,
She packed her bag
And off she went.

She left behind her
A tooth fairy mist.
Oh she was
So badly missed.

The tooth fairy usually
Exchanged teeth for money.
When this didn't happen
The results were not funny.

Parents sighed,
Children cried.
No money for sweets
Or other such treats.

Tempers frayed.
As the tiny teeth stayed.
All was gloom,
Until suddenly- BOOM!

The tooth fairy was back.
Quick as a flash,
She collected all the teeth
And gave out all the cash.

So the world was put right,
That's how it will stay,
Until the next time she goes
On holiday!

73

# Losing Your Head

If your head falls off,
Quick, stick it back on,
For once you lose it
It will be gone.

It will send you emails
From famous places,
Boasting of its successes
In 'Heads Only' races.

It will mouth off
About this and that
And send you selfies
In a strange sunhat.

It will taunt you by reminding you
How your life used to be
Before your head fell off
Then set off to be free.

And you will be stuck
With a headache at home.
Just a lonely body
All on its own!

# The Bingly Bangly Song

Bingly Bangly Bing,
Bingly Bangly Bong.
You can't go wrong
With this Bingly Bangly song.

Once you know the words
You can sing along.
You can't go wrong
With this Bingly Bangly song.

Bingly Bangly Bing,
Bingly Bangly Bong.
You can't go wrong
With this Bingly Bangly song.

# The Pack

Chocolate Brownie bites,
Greeny growls,
Yellowy fights,
Bluey howls,
Reddy races,
Purply yelps,
Orangey chases,
Mighty Whitey helps.

# TimeLine

Start time, take your time,
Long time, loads of time.
Find time, a fine time,
School time, best time of your life?

Playtime, work time,
Lunchtime, home time.
Teatime, bedtime,
Sleep time, get up time.

Breakfast time, summer time,
Christmas time, fun time.
Spend time, rest time,
Time for reflection.

Don't waste time, save time,
You can't stop time.
Keep time, time up,
No time, timed out!

# Four

Four quarters,
Four seasons,
Four good reasons
For loving Four
Forever more.

Firstly, he's unforgettable.
Secondly, he's so forgiving.
Thirdly, he's full of information.
Fourthly, "For he's a jolly good fellow."

You won't forget him.
Formidable,
Forceful
Four.

# Soggy Shoes

Soggy shoes,
Fell into a boggy shoes,
Drenched by a shaking doggy shoes,
Toppled off a bridge, loggy shoes,
Battled with a wet hoggy shoes,
Soaked by a cold foggy shoes,
Splashed by a jumping froggy shoes.
Such soggy shoes!

# Twenty Words

## Twenty Words About Holes

A hole is an absence
Of cloth,
Or space,
Or ground,
Or someone who is
No longer to be found.

# Twenty Words About No

No.
Such a short, simple word.
No.
So negative,
So final.
No.
No?
Why not yes?
Let me Guess?
NO!

# Twenty Words About Starfish

Occasionally at night
Starfish drop from the skies
Into the vast oceans,
Like heavenly raindrops
Spreading light into the depths.

# Twenty Words About Kids

Kids are baby goats.
Baa, bleat,
Baa, bleat,
They repeat
Over and over,
As they munch
On grass and clover.

# Twenty Words About Okay

Two letters short form,
Four letters long form.
O.K?
Okay!
Turn short form OK around,
It's K.O.
KnockOut.
O.K?
Okay!

# Twenty Words About Slippers

After my dad died
I wore his slippers
For a year or two.
They helped me to fill his shoes.

# Twenty Words About Top Toast Topping

Not beans, not jam.
Not cheese, not ham.
Just make it sticky,
Call the bees!
Give me licky honey please!

# The World Of Books

## Reading

Where will reading take you?
Every country,
Every culture,
Every place,
Every race.
Everywhere you place your eyes
Replaces the places
You can't place your feet,
With endlessly fascinating people
For you to meet.
Reading takes you
Everywhere.

# Go On

Go on, go on,
Just have a go.
Go on, go on,
You can you know.
Go on, go on,
Before you know it,
Go on, go on,
You'll be a poet!

# Oh

Oh the places you go
As you sway to and fro,
Thinking marvellous thoughts
In your head.

Oh the places you see
And the way you feel free,
Every night when you go
To your bed.

Before you switch off the light
And hug your ted tight,
You know
Just what you need.

To open a book,
To look and look,
For you have learned
To read!

# This Is Me

Love in my heart,
A football at my feet.
Put a book in my hand
And I am complete.

# Poet

Writer, exciter, poet!
You know it
can be tough.
No ideas?
Brain like fluff?
But
When the muse strikes,
The flames flash,
You dash it down,
All that's been in your head,
And you didn't even know it.
Then you're a poet!

# Funkadelipcious

Poets are playful,
Rhythmical, swayful,
With swathes of words
You'll never have heard.

Like lompiosity,
Prepinkity,
Tellacious,
Mimp.

Hoskatot,
Spromping,
Slarkful,
And
Slimp.

Poets are playful,
Rhythmical, swayful,
Making up words
You'll never have heard.

Poets are Funkadelipcious!

93

# Warning

Poems can disrupt and disturb.
Have you only ever heard
Happy ones, funny ones,
Poems to make you giggle
And wriggle
And fall off your chair?

Poems you want to share
Because they're
Hilarious,
Tattifilarious,
Making your smile
As wide as a mile?

Have you only heard
Comical, bomical, tromical poems
That even serious sloths would like?

Well you should know,
There are others.
Sad poems and happy poems
Are sisters and brothers.
And you will find those sad poems,
Or maybe they will find you,

For laughter and tears are never far apart.
That's what they say.
And it's true.

# A Mark On A Page

A mark on a page
Will get you started.

A mark on a page means:
Don't be downhearted.

For you are a writer,
You've made your mark.

You are a writer,
And that's a start.

# Sports And Hobbies

## Sports

Tennis:
What a racket.
Cricket:
Don't be stumped.
Basketball:
Keep bouncing around.
Pole vault:
The rise and fall.
Rugby:
Try, try and try again.

# Swimming

I couldn't swim
Until I was eighteen.
Not at all,
Not one stroke.

I was scared of drowning.
Scared to push out
Into the deep.
Scared that it was I
That the water would keep,
That I would go under.
Swimming filled my brain
With thunder.

# The Dancer

Explode into life
With a shimmy and a shiver.
Strut your funky stuff
With a jump and a quiver.

Every step feels
So safe and secure.
It's boogie wonderland
As you glide across the floor.

For you are a dancer,
You love to move.
Your soul sings sweetly
As you get into the groove!

# Musical Instruments

Playful pianos,
Triumphant trumpets,
Reedy recorders,
Clashing cymbals,
Clacking castanets,
Groovy guitars,
Beating bongos,
Vigorous violins,
Cheerful cellos,
All of them calling:
"Hello,
Have a go!"

# Bread

I have a happy head
When I fill it full of bread.
Baguette, sandwich,
Naan or panini.
It doesn't matter much to me.
I just like putting bread,
Inside my head.

# Pottering

Pottering is not about pottery,
Potting or putting.
Neither is it off-puttingly potty.
Pottering is about moving
From one relaxing activity to another.

Pottering is not about Harry Potter,
The boy who lived,
But living
The good life,
The stress free life.

It's about adopting
A Sunday afternoon mindset,
Any time, anywhere
That you care
To potter.

It's not about achieving all that much.
It's more about getting back in touch
With friends,
Family, nature,
Yourself.

So dust down your
"Take it easy" shelf,
And take it easy,
With relaxing, chillaxing
Pottering.

# Toast

Oh delicious, hot toast,
I love it the most.
Inland or on the coast,
It's the best breakfast gift
You can give as a host.
I will always boast
About my beautiful, buttery toast!

# Party Games

Pasta parcel,
Pass it around.
Pasta parcel,
What will be found?
Pasta parcel,
The music stops.
Pasta parcel,
The package drops.
Pasta parcel,
Just don't forgetti,
In pasta parcel
The prize is spaghetti!

# Green For Ever

## Looking out

I'm sitting in a chair
Looking out at the trees.
Not a thing seems to stir,
Not a hint of a breeze.

But if I look more closely
The blades of grass
Are all a quiver,
Constantly vibrating
Like the ripples
Of a river.

While overhead the sky
Is a bright, searing blue.
Not a cloud mars the beauty
Of this perfect morning view.

# Planning

If we want to save the planet
We have to plan it.
We can't just hope
That we'll be able to cope.
We won't.
So please,
Let's plant more plants and trees.
Let's not poison the bees
With pesticides.
Let's decide
To be keen
To be green.
If we want to save the planet
We have to plan it!

# Out of This World

Have you seen the stars
Shining on a clear night?
Glistening diamonds of utmost beauty,
They gleam
With the purest light.

Most are other suns,
So far away,
Invisible in our world
During the day,
When our sun
Dominates,
Radiates
Its own light and heat.

But at night
Those stars
In our eyes
Are the ultimate
Celestial treat!

109

# Green

Green, it's all green.
The trees, the fern, the forest, the wood,
The hedge, the leaf.
It's all good
When it's green.

Grey, it's all grey,
When our greenery is stolen away.
Despoiled, destroyed, disinherited,
Distraught.
Some say grey's okay.

But we say that's wrong.
Green is the colour of the world's song.
Green, it's all green.
The trees, the fern, the forest, the wood.
Only when it's green can the world be good!

# Our Earth

The Earth's always moving,
So scientists say.
The Earth's too polluted,
It's a dangerous day.
The Earth's a globe,
You can fly right around.
The Earth's overheating,
Scientists have found.
The Earth's delicate,
However resilient it seems.
Our Earth may recover,
But only if actions follow dreams.

# After The Rains

Surprise!
Blue skies!
Or at least
It's not
Totally grey
Today.
Hip, hip, hooray!

# The Lean Green Eco Machine

We're the lean, green eco machine,
Saving the planet's our ultimate dream.
We can't do it all,
But we'll do all we can.
Healing the Earth is our beautiful plan.

It's time to end the desecration
Of all the destructive deforestation.
May rewilding plant the seeds
Of our planet's vital needs.

Plastic pollution has to stop
If nature's ever again
To come out on top.
Too many species
Are lost and dying.
No wonder our incredible
Planet is crying.

114

Flooding and burning
Are out of control.
Global warming
Is humanity's own goal.
So yes we will make a fuss,
As the fate of the Earth is up to us.

We're the lean, green eco machine,
Saving the planet's our ultimate dream.
We can't do it all,
But we'll do all we can.
Healing the Earth is our beautiful plan.

# Riddle Answers

Riddle Me One = Crabs
Riddle Me Two = Rainbow
Riddle Me Three = School
Riddle Me Four = Ancient Romans

# Martin Olsson

www.olssonmartin.wixsite.com/professorillustrator

Also by Andy Tooze

# The Poetry Bug

*Published by Matador 2016*

Also by Andy Tooze

# The Poetry Bug Stikes Again

*Published by Matador 2018*

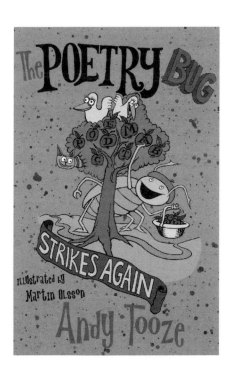